Football Fitness

FOOTBALL FITNESS

ADE MAFE

B▨XTREE

Advice for the Reader

Before following any medical, exercise or dietary advice contained in this book, it is recommended that you consult your doctor if you suffer from any health problems or special conditions or are in any doubt as to its suitability.

B XTREE

First published in 1998 by Boxtree, an imprint of Macmillan Publishers Ltd, 25 Eccleston Place, London, SW1W 9NF and Basingstoke

Associated companies throughout the world

ISBN 0 7522 2444 1

Copyright © Chelsea Communications Ltd, 1998

Photographs © copyright Jon Nicholson except pages 82-3, 84 and 85, Science Photo Library, page 88 Multipower Fitness & Nutrition and page 89 Allsport

The right of Ade Mafe to be identified as the author of this work has been asserted by him in accordance with the Copyright, Designs and Patents Act 1988.

9 8 7 6 5 4 3 2 1

A CIP catalogue record for this book is available from the British Library

Nutrition Advisor: Susannah Olivier

Designed by DW Design

Printed and bound in Great Britain by The Bath Press

Contents

Ade Mafe

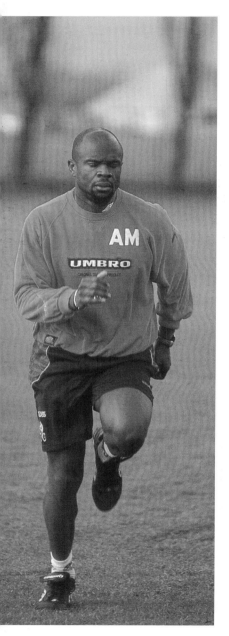

Ade Mafe, fitness and conditioning coach to Chelsea Football Club, has had a long career in athletics and professional fitness training. In 1984, at the age of seventeen, he finished eighth in the 200m at the Los Angeles Olympics. He still holds the record as the youngest British male ever to compete in an Olympic track and field final. It was the beginning of a twelve-year career during which Ade competed in track events all over the world while training six days a week for four to five hours a day.

Ade's impressive list of achievements and records in athletics includes: European Junior Champion at the 200m and 4 x 400m in 1985; holder of the British junior record for the 200m; European Indoor gold medallist over 200m in 1989, 200m silver medallist in 1985; World Indoor 200m silver in 1985 and 1989 and bronze medallist in 1991; holder of the world indoor record for the 4 x 200m with Linford Christie, John Regis, and Darren Braithwaite set in 1991; bronze medallist at the Commonwealth Games in Auckland, New Zealand in 1991, and member of the World Championship Gold medal winning team in Tokyo in 1991.

At the age of twenty-six, Ade retired from competitive athletics. Using his first-hand experience of fitness training, and the knowledge he had gained from training under coaches such as Ron Roddan, who coached Ade and Olympic champion Linford Christie, he became a personal trainer. Over the next three years he worked with forty clients aged from eight to eighty.

In 1996 Mafe was approached by Ruud Gullit who was looking for a fitness trainer for Chelsea Football Club. Ade developed a special fitness and conditioning programme for the squad, and now trains with them every day and before every match. At the end of his first season, Chelsea won the FA Cup, beating Middlesbrough 2-0 at Wembley. The following season they returned to Wembley to win the Coca-Cola Cup and won the European Cup-Winners' Cup.

Introduction

It may not be apparent to the casual observer, but there is a revolution going on in English football. Managers such as Ruud Gullit when he was at Chelsea, Arsene Wenger at Arsenal and Roy Hodgson at Blackburn, all of whom have either played or coached in Europe, have introduced new methods regarding the fitness and conditioning of their players. Many of these techniques have been well known in the fitness and athletics communities for some time, but British football seems to have been oblivious to them. Two years ago, when Ruud Gullit brought me in to be responsible for the physical state of the players, Chelsea became one of the few clubs in the Premiership to employ a special fitness and conditioning trainer – a position that is commonplace on the continent.

When I started to look into football fitness, it soon became apparent that the majority of English players had not previously paid much attention to their physical condition. As long as a top-class footballer played skilfully, his fitness and conditioning were of secondary importance. Football coaches and managers, with so many other things to deal with, tended to pay little attention to fitness training, pushing the responsibility onto the club physiotherapists whose speciality it wasn't. Bad physical conditioning and lack of maintenance led to injuries and early retirement for many unfortunate players.

Today and in the future you will find players who are able to play longer and keep themselves healthier, thanks to good body maintenance. The earlier he starts on a proper football fitness programme, the less likely it is that injury will stop a promising young player from realising his dreams in the game. Someone once said to me that the body is like a car engine: if you don't maintain it properly it will break down, especially if you are pushing it to its limits. So MAINTENANCE of the body is a very important aspect of total football fitness.

When I joined Chelsea I was surprised how many players were unaware of CONDITIONING training. It's not enough just to push the players to the limits of their endurance; football fitness training should be specific, mimicking the demands placed on the body during the course of a game. When Brazilian player Branco left Middlesbrough, the press reported that he complained "I am not a horse!" He was used to a sophisticated training programme rather than just endless running exercises.

Steve Clarke told me about how he used to train in Scotland when he was younger:

"We never used to touch a ball in the first week, it was just run, run, run. We used to go up into the hills and go on cross-country treks. We used to do turnarounds up hills and hill sprints, literally hundreds of them. It was hard running. It's all changed now – the standard of football has improved and fitness training has become a lot more technical and scientific. I know I wouldn't be playing now if I had to do the running I used to do then. We were fit though."

Today's game is becoming increasingly competitive. At a professional level, the sums of money involved are greater than ever before and the difference between winning and losing becomes more important to clubs and players alike. As the competition for places in the top clubs becomes more intense, bigger squads and the influx of foreign players are adding to the pressure. For many years, football and fitness have gone hand in hand for continental clubs because the stronger, faster and fitter the player, the more likely it is that games will be won, not lost. But this doesn't just apply to professional players; it is true for players at every level and age. This book will show what you can do to improve your ENDURANCE, STRENGTH, SPEED and AGILITY and so become a better player.

Finally, fitness training needs fuel: good, wholesome food. DIET will play a vital role in my quest to help you improve the physical aspects of your game. Great developments have been made at Chelsea and other clubs regarding the players' diets. The influx of foreign players has had a major impact in this area. We have a lot to learn from the Mediterranean diets of players such as Zola and Vialli.

This book is aimed at football players of all ages, from eight years and upwards, at all levels of fitness. The exercises can benefit anyone, from schoolboys to Sunday League players, as well as professionals, as long as you follow the first rule of fitness training: take care. Don't strain your body by trying to do too much too soon, or you will end up less fit, not more. Obviously an eight-year-old will not be as strong as a seventeen-year-old, and if you play once a week you won't be as fit as someone who plays three times a week, so scale down the exercises and their intensity to suit your level. I will give you rough guidelines on this throughout the book. As far as strength is concerned, it's universally recognised that children under sixteen, and indeed any children who are still growing, should not train with weights. Body weight exercises are a good alternative and I have given a rough scale, according to age, for their use.

I have tried to make these exercises as fun and varied as possible. Remember, the better conditioned you are, the more effectively you will be able to use your football skills on the pitch, and the more you will enjoy the game.

Preparation

Equipment

The wonderful thing about football and the reason it's played all over the world is its simplicity. All you need is a ball and a goal – whether that means a tin can and two sweaters, or a Mitre ball and professional goal posts. The same is true of football fitness training. Most of the exercises can be done on the pitch with no equipment, or simple markers such as cones.

Grass is the preferred surface for training as it is firm, but also has some give. Concrete should be avoided if at all possible as prolonged pounding on a hard surface can cause damage to the knee and ankle joints. Sprung wooden floors are a better alternative if you have to train indoors.

I will talk in more detail about gym equipment in the BODY STRENGTH AND CONDITIONING chapter.

Footwear

Boots

There are hundreds of different football boots on the market. Like trainers, there are fashions for different styles and colours, even among professional players. But when buying a boot the comfort of fit is the most important consideration, not how it looks. A player's feet are the most important part of his or her body and if you don't look after them they will not serve you very well for very long. It is vital that your boots fit well and provide good support, particularly to the arch of your foot, instep and heel. Always buy the best you can afford.

Cross-trainers

On surfaces where football boots are not suitable, such as tarmac, trainers are the best substitute. Again, make sure they support your foot properly. If you have a pair that you have already been using for football training, look at where they have worn out the most. When you buy a new pair, make sure they have extra reinforcement in those areas.

Running

Good running shoes are essential for the long distance runs that you will do during pre-season training, as well as those training sessions that include running on dry grass or hard ground. Try and find a shop that's owned and operated by runners. The benefits of specialist knowledge are worth shopping around for.

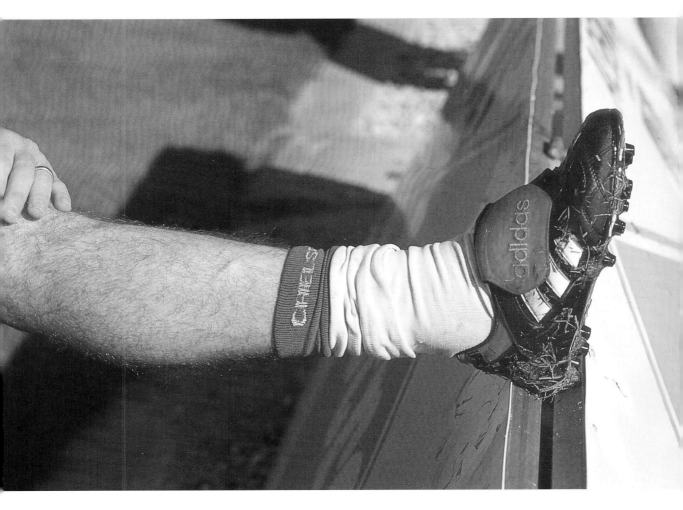

Warm-up and Body Maintenance

1. Starting off –
the warm-up

Blefore either a training session or game the muscles have to be prepared for the vigorous demands that will be placed on them. First of all, get loose and warm with a light jog lasting three to four minutes. Make huge circles with your arms while you're jogging to get blood flowing into the muscles in your upper body as well. Increased blood flow to the muscles will literally warm them up, making the fibres slightly more elastic. You get a better stretch from a warm muscle and reduce the risk of injury, so don't start stretching when you're still cold – get warm first.

2. Stretching

You should stretch before and after every exercise session, wether you are going to be running, football training or actually playing a match. Most people are relatively inflexible. If you spend hours every day sitting in a chair for example, your knees will be bent and the hamstrings, the muscles in the back of your thigh, will be relaxed and shorter than they would be if you were standing up. Over time, those muscles can become shorter than they could or should be and bad posture will be the result. That's just one example of one muscle group.

It is vital that all the muscles you are going to use are stretched to their maximum length and made as elastic as possible before you start exercising. After a work-out or game, when your muscles will have been contracting and relaxing repeatedly, you need to stretch again, otherwise those muscles will remain slightly contracted and you'll feel stiff and sore the next day. Stretching allows joints to move through a greater range of motion, making you a more efficient player and one less prone to injury. Stretching benefits running, jumping, tackling; basically every movement you make in a game.

You'll get a better stretch if the muscle is as relaxed as possible before you begin, so concentrate on that. If a stretch starts to hurt that's your body warning you that muscle damage might be about to occur. Your muscles will involuntarily contract to protect themselves and you won't be able to get a decent stretch.

- Stretch slowly and gently
- Take the stretch to the point where you feel a mild tension in the muscle or muscle group being stretched
- If it hurts, ease off – over-stretching can lead to strained muscles
- Hold each stretch for six to ten seconds
- Stretch each muscle/muscle group twice – you should feel a slight loosening and get a better stretch the second time

Stretching may seem boring, but it is essential. When I first came to Chelsea very few players did enough stretching. All they wanted to do was play football, but I managed to persuade them that stretching is very important in terms of injury prevention. Dan Petrescu is an avid stretcher, sometimes spending up to an hour a day stretching.

Calves

Your calf is made up of two principal muscles: the gastrocnemius sits high up below the knee, and can be quite chunky; the soleus is the longer muscle – and sits behind the gastrocnemius. The Achilles tendon which is the bottom end of the gastrocnemius, attaches the muscle to the bones in your heel.

Gastrocnemius Stretch

This is done best up against a wall or post, or with a partner, as you'll need something to push against to get a good stretch. Place one foot in front of the other, toes pointing forwards, so the feet are about two feet apart. Bend the front knee but keep the back leg straight. Keeping the heel of the rear foot flat on the floor, push against the wall/post or your partner* to drive that heel into the ground. If you don't feel a stretch in the back of your calf, slide the rear leg back a few more inches until you do. Change legs, and repeat.

Soleus and Achilles Tendon Stretch

This stretch is the same as for gastrocnemius, but instead of keeping the rear leg straight, bend it and keep on bending until you feel a stretch down towards your heel. Make sure that you keep your heel on the floor. Change legs and repeat.

Thighs

There are four principal muscles in the front of your thigh: vastus medialis, vastus intermedius, vastus lateralis and rectus femoris. They are collectively known as the quadriceps or quads for short.

Standing Quadriceps Stretch

Standing up, grab hold of your ankle, right hand to right foot, and pull your heel in to your backside as far as you can. Keep your knees together and your back straight. If you don't feel much of a stretch down the front of your thigh, try and stand up as straight as you can. This movement will make you tilt your pelvis forward slightly, accentuating the stretch in your quads. Hold, change leg and repeat. Hold onto a post or wall if you can't balance on one leg.

Side-lying Quadriceps Stretch

This is slightly more effective than a standing quad stretch. It's also easier because you don't have to worry about keeping your balance. Lie down on your side, taking all the weight off the muscles, and pull back the top leg to your backside, using your free arm for balance. Change legs and repeat.

Hamstrings

The hamstrings are the group of muscles in the back of your thigh. When I was growing up I always thought that the best way to stretch the hamstrings was to bend over and touch the toes, keeping the legs straight and bouncing up and down. Recent research has proved this type of 'ballistic' stretching to be potentially dangerous and nowhere near as effective as the 'passive' stretching recommended here. Ballistic stretching of the hamstrings puts a lot of stress on the lower back and can cause microscopic tears in the muscles, which could lead to more serious damage later.

Lying Hamstring Stretch

Lie flat on your back. Bend one knee and put that foot flat on the floor. This will help to keep your lower back flat while you stretch. Lift the other leg and get hold of your calf just below the knee. Trying to keep this leg straight, pull it towards you. You should aim, eventually, for ninety degrees of flexion at the hip – i.e. your leg pointing straight up at right angles to your body.

It's quite likely that your hamstrings won't be flexible enough to do this properly at first. If you find yourself having to get into all sorts of contortions to hold on to your leg, try this other method: Get yourself a skipping rope or towel. In the same position as outlined above, place the rope or towel under the instep of the leg you want to stretch. Take one end of the rope/towel in each hand, and, keeping that leg straight and relaxed, lie back and slowly pull your leg up. The first place you will probably feel this stretch will be behind your knee. This is perfectly normal – the tendons that attach your hamstring muscles to your bones run through the knee joint and into the bones in the lower part of your leg.

Standing Hamstring Stretch

If the ground is too wet for the lying hamstring stretch, this is the best alternative. Place one foot in front of the other about two feet apart, toes pointing forwards. Keep the front leg straight and rear leg slightly bent. Tilt forward from the hips and place your hands on the rear leg just above the knee. Keep bending the rear leg so that the majority of your weight is on that foot. You should feel a stretch down the back of the straight leg. Once again hold, change and repeat.

Partner Hamstring Stretch

You can also stretch the hamstring with the help of a partner. Stand facing each other about three feet apart. Have your partner interlock his fingers, palms up at waist height, to make a cradle for your heel. Now put one foot into this cradle and straighten that leg. Have a slight bend in the knee of the standing leg. Try and keep your hips square on to your partner, then tilt forward, keeping your back as straight as you can, hands resting on the extended leg, until you feel a stretch down the back of the thigh. If no tension is felt, ask your partner to raise his hands till tension is felt in the hamstring. If you're the partner in this exercise don't be tempted to have a laugh by throwing your mate's leg up in the air so he falls over backwards. That's a perfect way to tear a hamstring, and they can take weeks to heal properly.

Glutes and Lower Back

The gluteus maximus – your backside – is the engine room that provides the initial, explosive power for a running stride or a jump. So it is vital that you maintain this area well.

Glutes Stretch

Sit down with your feet out in front of you, take one leg and, bending the knee, pull the leg close to your body, placing your foot over the opposite thigh. Place your arms around the bent leg and pull it in as close to your body as you can. You should feel the outside of your bum stretching. Hold, change and repeat.

If you do not feel a tension here you can twist your body so that you are facing your bent leg side, using your free arm behind you for balance, as shown.

Lower Back Stretch

Lying flat on your back, roll both knees up to your head. Hooking your arms behind your knees hold your legs as close to your head as possible, making sure that your backside is off the ground. Hold and repeat.

Hip Abductor Stretch

Your abductors are the muscles in the outside of your hip. They are very important in providing the ability to execute the perfect side step and they also provide your hips and pelvis with vital stability – stability that can also help keep stress off your lower back.

Lying on your back, put your arms out from your sides crucifix style. Then, trying to keep your shoulders in contact with the ground, lift one leg so the foot is pointing straight up. Now, slowly lower that leg to the side and over your other leg until it touches the floor. Try to keep your shoulders on the ground. Slowly return your leg to the vertical, then return it to the floor and repeat with the other leg.

Some people will find it hard to keep their shoulders in contact with the ground. This is due to a lack of flexibility in your thoracic spine – the middle section that has ribs attached to it. Don't force your shoulders down – let gravity do the work. Eventually it will get easier.

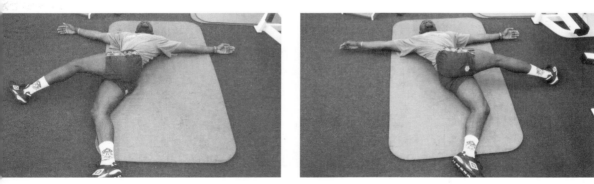

Groin

How many times have you read in the papers that a top player has been sidelined with a 'groin strain'? If you think about all the lunging that goes on in football – such as when making a tackle or stretching to intercept a pass – it's perhaps surprising that more players don't suffer this injury. There are two muscle groups to be dealt with here: hip adductors and hip flexors. The adductors are on the inside/top of your thigh. They are the muscles that are doing most of the work when you do a side-footed kick. Your hip flexors are at the front/top of your thigh. As you lift your foot off the floor, when running or walking for example, your hip flexors are doing the work. Strong hip flexors are also crucial to kicking power as you bring your leg through to strike the ball. Since they do so much work during a game, it's especially important to stretch them.

Hip Flexors

Kneel down on one knee on a mat (or other soft surface). Put the non-kneeling foot well forward, keep your trunk nice and upright, and rest your hands on the front knee. Now rotate your pelvis forwards until you feel a tension at the top/front of your thigh. You can also ease your trunk forwards slightly to accentuate the stretch. This stretch is much easier to do than it is to describe in words. Change legs and repeat.

Adductor Stretch

This is an easy stretch, and you can do both legs at once. Sit on the floor, with the soles of your feet pressed against each other, knees pointing outwards. Holding on to your ankles, use your elbows to push down on the insides of your knees. Push until you feel a stretch on the inside/top of your thighs. Hold, relax and repeat.

Alternative Adductor Stretch

Stand up with your legs wide apart, toes pointing forwards. Bend one knee and put the weight of your body on that leg. Keep the body upright and the other leg stationary. You should feel the stretch up the inside of the straight leg. Change legs and repeat.

N.B. If you do not feel tension in the muscles while doing these stretches, there are two possible explanations; you're very flexible already, or you're not doing them correctly. Unless you're also a gymnast, the first possibility is unlikely. As long as you're aware of which muscles you're trying to stretch, you'll get it right eventually. So, persevere.

Out to In   In to Out

3. Mobility

The knee joint, protected by a layer of synovial fluid

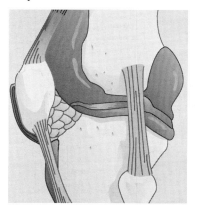

The next stage of the warm-up is the mobility exercises, which are essential for body maintenance. These exercises loosen up the joints and make the newly stretched muscles familiar with the movements that will be required of them during the game. These exercises also help avoid muscle strain and injury.

The most important joints in football are the ankles, knees and hips, the latter two taking the most stress in the course of a professional's career.

The synovial fluid in the ankle and knee joints lubricates the joints and prevents friction between bones and cartilage. Before exercise it is thick and gooey in consistency. During exercise, because of the heat generated in the joints, it thins and becomes less viscous, making it more effective. This is the state we have to get it in before you start playing or running fast.

During pre-exercise stretching you will have cooled down, so it's a good idea to warm up again with a quick jog before continuing with the following mobility exercises. Do a selection from the list, each over a distance of about fifteen to twenty metres.

Out to In:
With a walking step, lift the knee up to the side and then round to the front, to draw an anti-clockwise circle before returning it to the ground.

In to Out:
Repeat the above, bringing the knee up at the front and round to the outside, drawing a clockwise circle.

Kick Straight Up:
With a walking step kick out in front of you, touching your foot with your hands. Do this alternately – one leg at a time. If you have tight hamstrings, take care.

Side Volleys:
Walking forwards make small side volleys as if kicking a ball.

Insides:
While walking flick the foot up and inwards touching it with the hand. Kick up with each foot alternately.

Kick Straight Up

Side Volleys

Insides

Outsides

Side-step

Outsides:
Do the same as with insides but flick the foot outwards.

Side Step:
Take sideways skipping steps.

Run backwards.

Jockeying:
Run backward jockeying or shuffling as you would when marking a player on the pitch. (The same can be done going forwards.)

High Knees:
Run, bringing the knees high with every step.

Running/Jockeying Backwards

High Knees

Flicks

Headers   Kicks Across   Knee to Shoulder

Flicks:

Run, kicking the ankles up to the backside with every step.

Touch the Floor:

While jogging forwards reach down to touch the floor alternately with both hands keeping your back as upright as possible – bend your knees to get down, rather than your spine.

Headers:

While running forwards do small imaginary headers using the neck muscles in three directions, forward, left and right.

Kicks Across:

While walking, kick each leg in turn across your body. If you have tight hamstrings you should take care while doing this exercise.

Knee to Shoulder:

While walking, bring the knee up towards the shoulder, behind the arm.

After this it would be good to stop and recover your breath before moving to the next stage of the session, which will raise the intensity and effort level. If your muscles still feel sore or there is any particular area that still needs work, use this time as a stretching break.

4. Final warm-up

After the mobility exercises we need to bring the body to the level of intensity that quality football training requires. A good way to do this is to spend about five minutes performing some of the previous running/mobility drills over a distance of about three to five metres, but with an added sprint over about ten metres. Increase the intensity until you are sprinting at about ninety per cent of your maximum sprinting speed.

When training with a team, you can organise a relay race, sprinting over ten to twenty metres for the final warm-up. If this is done with a forfeit of say twenty press-ups for the losers it will heighten the competition and get the running to a suitable intensity.

Games such as tag are another possible variation for the final warm-up.

5. Pre-match warm-up

Before a Premiership fixture, I only have about twenty minutes to warm the team up. Players can use up precious reserves of nervous energy during the warm up, energy that should be saved for playing the vital game that is coming up. Of this twenty minutes there has to be at least five to eight minutes of actual football, so that the players can get a feel of the ball. I spend the rest of the time going through the routines I have just described but shortened, and intensified so that we can fit everything in.

A typical pre-match warm-up

Jogging/light mobility...1 min
Stretching...6 min
Mobility..2 min
Mobility with sprints...2 min
Stretching...2 min
Sprints/reaction drills ....2 min
Football...5-8 min

Chelsea player/manager Gianluca Vialli believes a routine such as this ensures that all the players have warmed up properly and are prepared – mentally and physically – for the game. I would recommend you do something similar in your pre-match warm-up. Save your energy for playing but make sure that every muscle is stretched properly and thoroughly warmed up.

Part 2

Endurance and Stamina – Pre-Season Training

1. Energy & endurance

In a football game you are running around almost constantly for ninety minutes. This requires stamina combined with the ability to sprint repetitively over short distances. (The average distance covered by a top class midfielder in a game is about six to nine miles.) You need to be able to maintain energy levels and concentration throughout the game, for as Ruud Gullit always said:

"It takes only a second to score a goal but that second might come in the first or the ninetieth minute of the game. It can make the difference between winning and losing."

Training for any sport is all about adaptation. If there are limits to how far human beings can adapt to the physical demands they make of themselves, no physiologist is going to put his head on the block and say what those limits are. The current world record for the men's marathon, for example, is just over two hours and six minutes. The world record for a half-marathon is under one hour. Can a man run a marathon in less than two hours? You can bet it will happen one day. And since I'm trying to make you a better footballer, I'm making the exercises in this book as specific to actually playing the game as I can. There's not much point in spending time on physical training that isn't relevant to the game – unless you're just doing it for fun, of course.

During a football match there are three systems at work that provide you with specific types of energy. 1 and 2 are both anaerobic, meaning they operate 'without oxygen'. Number 3 is aerobic which means 'with oxygen'.

1) The ATP-CP system is for high intensity, short bursts. ATP-CP stands for (and it's quite a mouthful!) adenosine triphosphate-creatine phosphate. These are chemicals that are broken down in the muscles to provide energy for about the first ten seconds of activity.

2) The anaerobic glycolysis system is for intermediate bursts of quite high intensity activity. Anaerobic glycolysis produces lactic acid, the formation of which provides fuel after the first ten seconds (when the ATP-CP system has been doing all the work). Many people still seem to think that a build up of lactic acid (or lactate) gives muscles that tired, heavy feeling. Some also see lactic acid as a waste product' that needs to be removed from working muscles. Neither is true. Lactic acid is being produced in your body all the time, and its concentrations rise after you've eaten a carbohydrate-rich meal (see the Diet section on page 84). About half the lactic acid you produce during a strenuous training session is used by the muscles to form glycogen – muscle fuel. So lactic acid is an important component of the energy creation business. However, as it accumulates in the blood, lactate starts to have a negative effect on your aerobic performance. Plenty of quality training can raise an athlete's tolerance of this lactate

accumulation, meaning they don't get tired as quickly and recover faster. Hill sprint repetitions are a good example of training designed to improve your tolerance, and anyone who's ever done these will know how tiring they are. For that reason it's a good idea to do this type of training at the end of a session, so that you have plenty of time to recover for the next one.

3) The aerobic system is for long efforts of low to moderate intensity. A 100-metre sprint uses ATP-CP and anaerobic glycolysis in about a 50-50 ratio and doesn't rely on oxygen at all, sprinters often holding their breath during an entire 100-metre race. But obviously Linford Christie could not carry on sprinting at top speed for miles and miles. A marathon runner uses the aerobic system almost exclusively.

After having sprinted hard we have to slow down to recover our breath. In a football match these recovery periods constitute the bulk of the playing time. Research in Japan showed how 70 per cent of a footballer's energy during a game was spent on low to moderate activity fuelled by the aerobic system. This level of activity relies principally on oxygen in your bloodstream converting glycogen (which is also in your blood and has been extracted from the food you have eaten) into energy in the muscles. It's not wholly dissimilar to the way energy is produced (as heat) when you burn something, where you need both fuel and oxygen for anything to happen.

The fitter you are, aerobically, the more effectively oxygen will be absorbed into your bloodstream and then pumped to the working muscles. Aerobic exercise gives your heart a work out, making it a more powerful pump. There are other benefits for the footballer of aerobic exercise: increased aerobic fitness helps increase blood flow to the muscles after a hard, fast sprint, bringing oxygen and other nutrients into the muscle and taking waste products out. This helps prepare your body for another short sprint, and since you're likely to be doing a high-intensity sprint every 90 seconds or so, you can see why recovery is so important.

During my career in athletics my coach Ron Roddan taught me that in training it's always best to try to reproduce the stresses on the body caused by the sport itself. As we have seen, football requires different energy systems to fuel the activity, so it's important to incorporate aspects of all those systems in your training. Most of the hard work on building up aerobic fitness – stamina – should be done pre-season. During the season you will need to maintain your levels of aerobic fitness while also concentrating on anaerobic fitness, skills training, tactics and mental fitness.

When I came to Chelsea I introduced a new pre-season training schedule. Part of that schedule was a method of training known as Fartlek – a Swedish word meaning 'speed play' – that consists of long runs, but of varying speeds. These I alternate daily with shorter, pitch-based running sessions, which allow the body to recover after the repetitive stress of the longer runs. Pitch-based intensive work also gives me the opportunity to train the players' anaerobic energy systems.

The idea of adapting training to the demands of the sport is now so well-established in other sporting fields, it seems strange that it has taken such a long time to take hold in British football. I think part of the reason for this is that football training was kept 'in house' with former players becoming trainers and passing on their methods to the next generation rather than taking on board new training techniques. The years when British teams were out of European football saw the continental clubs bring in specialists in nutrition and fitness conditioning to give their players every advantage.

"When I started playing the fittest players were the ones who could run the hardest for the longest, where now we run for speed, reaction, endurance and stamina. The attitude and approach have completely changed."
Steve Orgrizovic, Coventry goalkeeper

2. Pre-season training programme

Below is an example of a pre-season training programme for the Chelsea squad, alternating fartlek and pitch sessions. The same exercises can be adapted to any football training programme, whether you are training once, three or five times a week.

WEEK 1

Day 1

Pick a route, ideally over grass and with hills. If you train with a team or group of friends, each one of you could create his own fartlek route. That way you wouldn't be covering the same ground time after time. Aim to spend 20-30 minutes on the course alternating between jogging and running at 75 per cent of your top speed (pretty much as you would during a game). Pick markers such as trees, paths, telegraph poles, lamp-posts, gates, benches etc. along the route so you can run from one to the other. Having jogged to the first marker sprint/stride at 75 per cent to the next (which should be 50 metres away). Then jog again to recover for about 30 seconds before striding to the next marker which should be 40 metres away. Basically the distances that you stride to should get shorter, not least

because you'll be getting more and more exhausted! Make the last sprint/stride over 10 metres, then jog recovery for 2 minutes before repeating the sequence from 50 metres down to 10 metres. Jog to recover for 30 seconds between each stride/sprint.

Day 2
Figure of Eight Repetitions
Starting in one corner of the pitch, run to the opposite diagonal corner, then along the goal line to the next corner and back across the pitch diagonally to the opposite corner. Do three sets of three repetitions, aiming to cover the distance in 75 seconds each time. (Give yourself a press-up forfeit for each second you're over 75). Rest for about one minute between each repetition, and two minutes between each set.

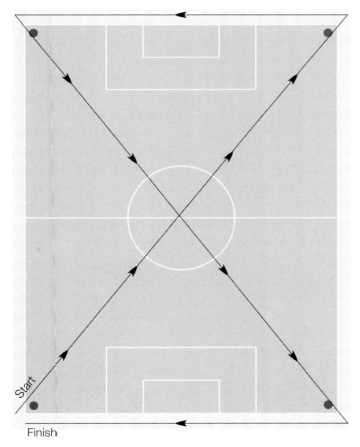

Day 3
Run for 20 minutes alternating throughout between 30 seconds jogging and 15 seconds at about 75 per cent of your top speed.

Day 4

Three sets of three full pitch runs in 60 to 65 seconds. Rest for one and a half minutes after each run and two minutes between each set.

Full Pitch Runs

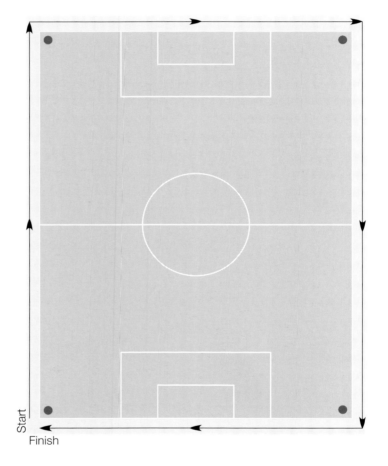

Start

Finish

Day 5

Same as Monday.

Day 6

Rest.

Day 7

Football only.

Alternative pitch sessions that can be fitted into your training schedule are:

Box to Box: Run from penalty box to penalty box. Repeat 10-12 times, taking 30-40 seconds to recover between runs.

Pitch Lengths: Run the length of the pitch. Repeat 10-12 times allowing 40-50 seconds to recovery time.

Line Runs: Start from the sideline down near the goal-line. Run across the pitch to each line of the penalty box and back to your starting point. The first turn will be at the eighteen-yard line of the penalty box, then the near six-yard of the box, the far six-yard line and the far eighteen-yard line then finally the other sideline. Repeat six to eight times with two minute rests in between.

Pitch Widths: From one sideline, run across the pitch in line with the D on the penalty box. Jog along the opposite sideline to the half-way line, run back across the pitch then jog back to your starting point. Repeat five to six times, resting for one minute between sets.

200/300/400/500 Metre Runs: Mark out the distance selected and run twice, resting for thirty seconds between the 200 or the 300 metre runs, and one minute at least between the 400 or 500 metre runs. Not a sprint, but a good paced run. Again do four to six pairs for the 200/300 metre runs and three or four pairs for the 400/500.

Goalpost Runs: Starting from the centre circle, run around both goalposts and then back to the centre circle. Aim to do the run in around 40 seconds. Repeat six to eight times, resting for one and a half minutes between runs.

Don't forget that plenty of stretching before and after the running sessions is vital. In my experience players have a tendency to develop lower back problems due to the demands of the game and tight hamstrings, hip flexors and quadriceps. Jogging and sprinting have different effects on the muscles, with the latter causing stronger contractions, greater stresses and a higher risk of injury. Gradually introducing faster runs can reduce the chances of muscle tears later on in the season.

3.   Rest

Rest is as important as training, especially if you are training a lot. It is vital that your energy levels are high at the beginning of a match. Over-training in the preceding days will cause fatigue on match day.

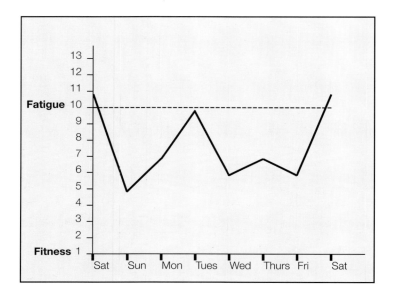

Above is a chart mapping the energy levels of a player who is playing on Saturday and training throughout the week. On the Saturday, the player runs his legs off during the game and is fatigued. He takes a day off on Sunday and by Monday he is fresh for training. After a good session on Monday and an even more intense one on Tuesday, his fatigue levels are sneaking back up again, but a day off on Wednesday restores the balance. A good session on Thursday and a light session on Friday show his level at 8, ready for the game on Saturday.

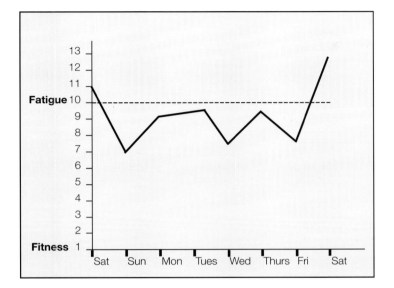

Here is a graph of a player who is training too hard and not giving himself enough rest. This player needs a decent amount of rest as he is constantly near the fatigue line and actually starts his game on Saturday in a fatigued state. The second half will probably see him substituted or reduced to walking pace.

It's a fine line to walk and it's easy to make mistakes. In my experience in football some teams suffer as a result of over-training. After a hard pre-season, they have a brilliant start to the season. But by the end of the season their form has dropped and their league position suffers because of their exhaustion. Their pre-season exertions and the number of games they have played have caught up with them.

So plan your training well. Take at least one day off a week, and if you are training six days a week, make one of those days a football session only, with no running exercises. If you are training three days a week, you should run for two of the three days.

During the season running training should concentrate on speed/endurance on Tuesday and sprinting on Thursday. This can be done after football skills/tactics training, allowing sufficient recovery time for the game on Saturday.

Part 3

Speed, Agility, Strength and Reaction Work– In-Season Training

Now we come to the serious stuff. After the pre-season training we have to sharpen up those reflexes and get the legs moving a little quicker. As the distances get shorter speed, agility, strength, and reaction are the names of the game. Sprints should play an important part of in-season training.

One important part of my training as an international track sprinter was technique. In the world of international athletics the difference between winning and losing was often down to milliseconds, hence every effort to get us from A to B as quickly and as efficiently as possible was made in the training.

Teaching sprinting technique in football is a harder proposition. Football is multi-directional and even if a player was taught the correct technique, in a game situation all that would be forgotten as he chased the ball. In any case, correcting sprint technique would not make the player quicker by any significant amount, so training in speed of reaction and agility is much more important.

1. Sprints for reaction

These are exercises to help sharpen up the body's reaction times. Use a clap or a whistle to start the sprint off. Always walk back and take enough time to recover after each run. It is the quality of the run that is important not the quantity.

From the following starting positions sprint for ten metres:

- Kneeling with hands behind the head
- Press up position
- Lying face down, hands behind the head, head on the starting line
- Lying down as above but with the feet on the starting line
- Lying face up, hands on stomach (both ways as above)
- Kneeling on one knee
- On hands and knees, facing in both directions
- Lying on your side in both directions
- Standing facing left, right or backwards
- Do a header before sprinting off
- Side-step out for two steps, then back to the start line before sprinting
- Run forwards for two steps, then backwards to the start line before sprinting for the ten metres

Franco Zola does reaction sprints as often as possible with me, as his speed over the first five metres is a vital asset to his game. Remember his goal at Highbury in the 1997 F.A. Cup semi-final against Wimbledon, where he turned the defender, Chris Perry? It's all about speed, reaction and agility.

2. Sprints for strength and endurance

Unless you're the goalkeeper, being able to sprint time and time again with minimal recovery is vital for your game. These exercises will help improve that ability.

Staggaroos

This is run for the length of the pitch, increasing in pace. As you run, vary from one change in pace at the half-way line, to three changes before the half-way line. Make the changes in pace gradual, rather than sudden, as you run. This will work your aerobic system.

Hill Runs

Short sprints of 10-20 metres up an incline will make the muscle work a lot harder, helping the initial explosive steps in a sprint. This type of exercise will work your anaerobic systems. Walk back down slowly, allowing longer recovery to maintain quality. Repeat in sets of three. Make sure a lot of time is spent stretching the calves before doing this session as the majority of the workload is put through them during this exercise, so they need to be flexible.

Explosions

These are sprints that are done on the run rather than from a stationary position. Jog for about 10 metres, then burst into a sprint for another 10 metres then slow to a jog again. Repeat for the length of the pitch, walking back to allow recovery time.

Penalty Box Doggies

From the goalmouth, sprint to each line including the D and jog back to the start. Rest for thirty seconds then repeat. Do three to four sets of four reps, resting for two minutes between each set.

Up and Downs

Put markers at 10, 20 and 30 metres then fast sprint to each jogging back to the start. Do three or four sets of two repetitions, resting for a minute between each set.

3. Agility, twisting and turning

As we all know, football is multi-directional. The ability to sprint is essential but equally important is the ability to turn at speed. Combining these two disciplines will improve your game. Here are some examples of sprint exercises that will help improve your agility. These exercises can be timed to add a little competition.

Use markers such as cones to mark out the course of the sprint. Each sprint should be over about 10-15 metres as the emphasis is on movement and speed, not overall distance.

Agility, twisting and turning exercises

All of these exercises should be done at a sprint of 80-90% of your maximum speed.

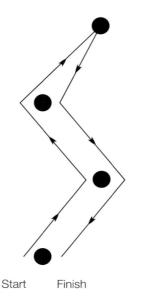

Start   Finish

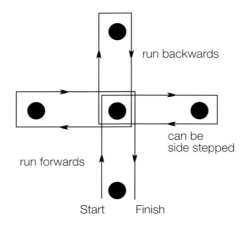

run backwards

can be
side stepped

run forwards

Start   Finish

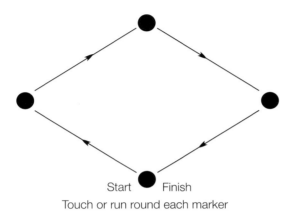

Start   Finish

Touch or run round each marker

Facing forwards, jockey between each marker.
This exercise can also be done jockeying backwards

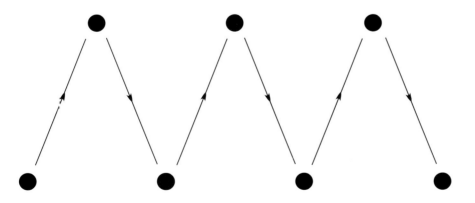

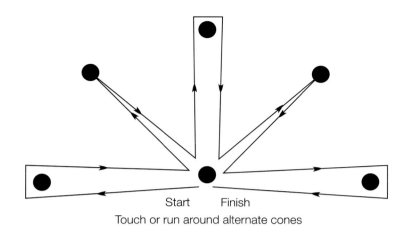

Start   Finish

Touch or run around alternate cones

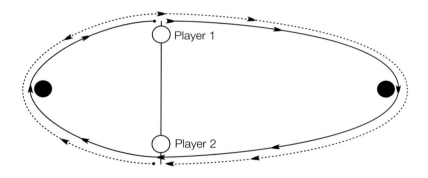

Two players stand on the starting line, facing in opposite directions. On the sound of the whistle, each player sprints around each cone and returns to his starting point (running in opposite directions). First past the starting line is the winner. This can then be repeated, changing direction. To make the turning more precise, place balls on top of the end cones, with a penalty for anyone who knocks the ball off.

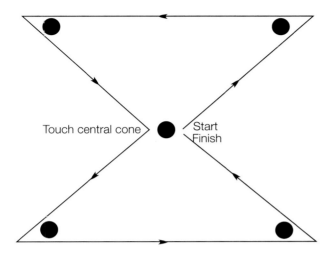

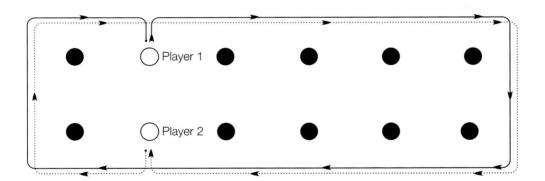

In this drill players stand facing each other about five metres apart. When a player's name is called, he and the player opposite him sprint in opposite directions down to the end of the line around the group and back to where they started. If, while they are running, 'Man on!' is called, the players have to change direction and return to their starting position. This command can be repeated as often as desired.

Part 4

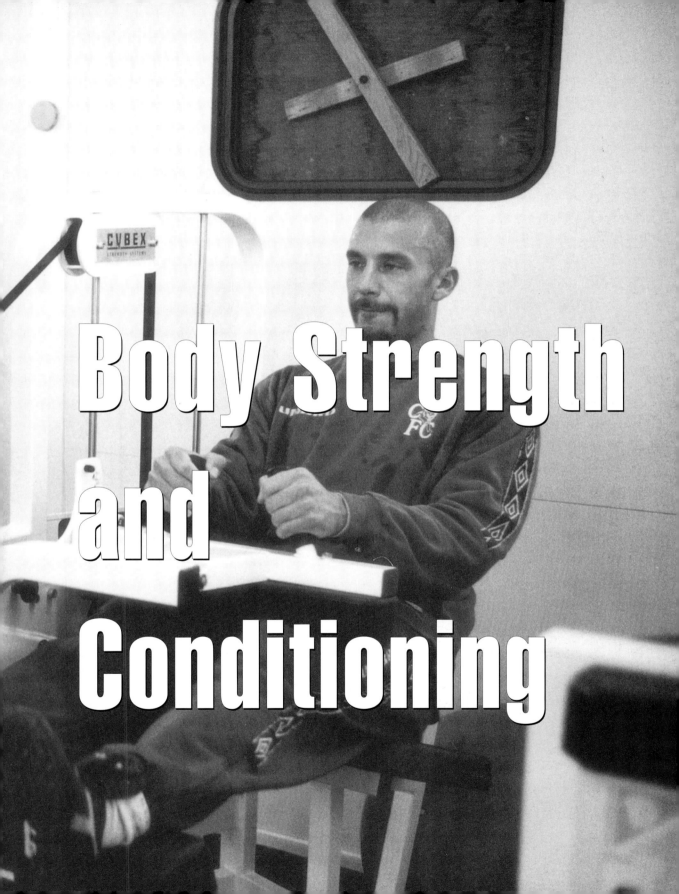

Body Strength and Conditioning

Football, especially in England, is a very physical game. All round body strength and fitness will help you survive the rough and tumble and reduce the risk of injury. Body strength and fitness can be improved through work in the gym or circuit training.

1. Gym work

When Roberto Di Matteo came to Chelsea he soon discovered that in English football the midfield is like a war zone, with players battling for control of the ball. This requires a lot of upper body strength that he didn't have. He had the maturity to realise this and we became regulars in the gym. I introduced various exercises to him and when he started to play well, several other players asked for the same workout routine. At the end of the season, Di Matteo gave me an Italian bracelet as a way of saying 'thank you' for all the work I had done with him through the year. I wear it every day with pride.

Increasingly these days, professional players are spending time in the gym working with weights both for protection and strength. Mark Hughes, Gianluca Vialli, Andy Myers, Gianfranco Zola, Celestine Babayaro, Paul Hughes and Eddie Newton all work out regularly in the gym. I have been devising plans for Mark Nicholls and Dennis Wise to help them with their upper body strength. These latter two are not especially big, so they have to be as strong as possible to handle themselves with confidence when it comes to challenging for the ball.

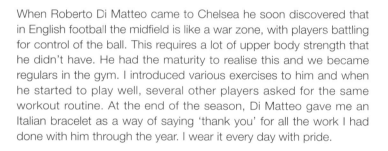

"I wish I had done all this weight training when I was younger because it gives me confidence on the pitch. It makes me feel strong and no matter how big the opposition is, I feel I can give as good as I get during a game if they feel like pushing me around."

Dennis Wise

What follows are the weights and gym exercises that I recommend for players over the age of seventeen. It's not a good idea to be lifting weights while you're still growing. The emphasis is on strength not size. In any case, if you're doing all the running exercises mentioned in the previous chapter, it's very unlikely that lifting weights will make your muscles that much bigger. In training with weights we're trying to overload the muscle using a combination of resistance (the weight), number of repetitions and speed of movement (slow!).

There are three basic types of muscular contraction: **concentric, eccentric** and **isometric.**

A **concentric** contraction is the most common and occurs when a muscle shortens as it contracts. If you perform a biceps curl, for example that's a concentric contraction of the biceps – the muscles on the front of your upper arm.

An **eccentric** contraction occurs when the muscle lengthens against a resistance. For example, once you've done a biceps curl and brought the weight up to your shoulder, you then have to lower it back to the start position. During this lowering phase the muscle lengthens and, provided you're controlling the speed, that's an eccentric contraction.

An **isometric** contraction occurs when you contract a muscle and it neither shortens nor lengthens, but stays still. Make a fist, hold your arm still and squeeze – that's an isometric contraction of the muscles in your forearm and probably your biceps too.

To find out how much weight you should be working with, you need to first find out what your 'one rep max' is for each exercise. One rep max is short for one repetition maximum and is the most weight you can lift or push just one time. In this section I'll be suggesting you work at various percentages of your one rep max.

To gain size and strength, the weights should be 80-90% of your one rep max with a low number of repetitions (up to eight) for about three to five sets. The lifting should be performed slowly with maximum effort. Rest is important, so take a good break in between sets – you'll need to otherwise you'll become too tired to complete the sets properly. If you feel that you could do with adding a few extra pounds of muscle to your frame, this is the sort of weight training you'll need to do. I would advise you to get your muscle-building work out of the way well before the season starts because it's a type of training that could impair your ability to perform all the aerobic and conditioning work that will follow.

Take a look at most professional players – although many are very strong, few have bulging muscles. Mark Hughes' thighs are an exception, but his strength is being able to shield the ball while holding opponents off and then turn, spin and shoot.

To gain power and endurance the weights should be at 60-70% of your one rep max, and the number of repetitions higher (15 to 20) for one to two sets. Here you can push the pace a little, with a shorter recovery period.

Weight training should be done up to two to three times a week, but not the day before a game, as your muscles will still be recovering when you play and you'll feel very 'heavy-legged'. In the off-season you should be working for size and strength, while in-season you can maintain your strength gains with a moderate session of single sets, 12-15 reps for each exercise at about 60% of your one rep max. Always work the big muscles first, i.e. thighs, chest and back, before moving on to smaller muscles such as calves, biceps and triceps. This is because many muscles act as synergists – they help with other exercises. For example, your triceps – the muscles in the back of your upper arm – play a significant role in a bench press, which is a chest exercise. If you had worked your triceps before your chest it may be that when you came to the bench press you would fail at a lower weight because your triceps were too tired rather than your chest.

Remember to warm up and stretch thoroughly before doing any of the following exercises. Regular breathing is vital. Generally speaking, breathe out on the effort.

The exercises that follow use equipment that should be available in your local gym or health club. When you first go to the gym, make sure that a member of staff shows you how to use all the equipment correctly and safely.

Legs

The calves, quads, hamstrings and groin are all used in the running, kicking, jumping, stopping, starting, twisting, and turning that is done on the pitch. Improving the strength in these areas will benefit your whole game.

Calves

Holding dumb-bells in each hand, with feet pointing forward shoulder width apart, go up on to your toes staying balanced and return to the ground.

N.B. If a calf raise machine is available at your gym, you have another option. In a seated position this will work soleus. In a standing position, as with the calf raises above, gastrocnemius will be worked.

Quads

When I arrived at Chelsea Ruud Gullit told me that he didn't want his players doing squats, or even leg press, to strengthen their quads. Even though squats are perfectly safe provided you do them properly, with assistance and don't already have knee problems (in fact many physiotherapists believe that they are safer than using the leg extension machine), Ruud was the boss. "Players take enough pounding in their knees from just playing football. Why add to it by doing squats?" he said. "Over a long period, the damage done will be doubled."

This book is designed to show you what we do here at Chelsea. When I started writing Ruud was in charge. He advocated leg extensions to strengthen the players' quads, and that's why they're in the book.

Leg Extension

Make sure that the seat of the leg extension machine is in the correct position, with your knee joint parallel with the lower hinge of the machine, and that you are comfortable. Starting with legs bent, straighten them until they are fully extended out in front of you. Hold here for a couple of seconds then return to starting position.

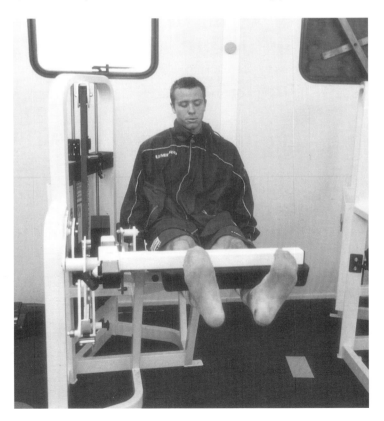

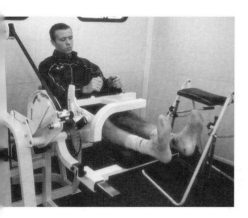

Hamstrings

The hamstrings – the muscles in the back of your thigh – are best worked with a leg curl machine. There are two types: one on which you lie face down (prone), and one on which you are seated.

In the prone position place your heels under the pads and have your knees just off the end of the bench. Make sure your hips stay in contact with the bench throughout the movement. Curl the rollers up to your backside and return them to the starting position.

In the seated position, make sure that the knee is parallel with the pivot on the lower arm of the machine. Put your ankles on top of the foot-pads and place the knee-pads securely on your knees. Bend at the knee, tucking your legs under the seat as far as you can, then return to the starting position.

Groin (Adductors)

The most common adductor exercise is performed using a seated adduction machine in a gym. Sit comfortably and place your legs in the holders. Bring your heels together and when contact is made return to the starting position.

Alternatively, standing upright, place a soft ball in between your feet. Squeeze your heels together and hold for a count of ten seconds. You could also do this seated with the ball between your knees.

Abdominals and Back

This area is known as the trunk and consists of the lower and middle back, and the stomach muscles (or abdominals). It's an area that is vital to keep strong as it connects the upper and lower parts of the body and has to deal with all the twisting and turning movements that football demands.

N.B. If you ever damage your back when training or playing, do something about it. Go and see you doctor and explain what happened. You may be prescribed rest and perhaps anti-inflammatory drugs as well. But these are treatments for the symptoms of a bad back, not the cause. Insist that you be referred to a physiotherapist who is better qualified to ascertain why you've hurt yourself. Armed with this knowledge, you can then take steps to make sure it doesn't happen again.

The following exercises will help strengthen the back and abdominals. Some people can do hundreds of abdominal exercises; other people find ten a strain. To work out how many you should be doing, perform as many reps as you can without stopping, (say 30); divide this number by three (10) and then multiply it by two (20). That's how many reps you will do for each set. Do three to six sets.

Thigh Slide

Lie on your back (ideally on a mat), with the soles of your feet on the floor. Bend your knees to ninety degrees and place your palms on your thighs. Lift your head off the mat until your shoulders are also off the mat. Keeping your chin tucked onto your chest, curl up until your shoulder blades come off the mat and you have slid your hands up as far as your knees. Hold for a second in this position, curl back down and repeat. Make sure you keep your head off the floor throughout. This exercise works rectus abdominis – the muscle that runs down your stomach from just under your ribs to the pubic bone in your pelvis.

Crunch

Lie on your back and lift your feet off the floor, bending your knees and crossing your legs in front of you. Place your hands on the sides of your head, and tuck your chin into your chest as above. Curl up until your elbows touch your knees. Try to keep your hips and legs still during the crunch. Keep a comfortable pace, not too quick but not too slow. And don't forget to breathe! This is another rectus abdominis exercise, but slightly harder than the thigh slide.

Heel Touch

Assume the same position as in the thigh slide but this time reach with your hands to touch your heels.

Lower Abdominals

Lying down, lift up your legs until your feet are directly above your hips. Placing your hands on the floor beside you for balance, slowly lift your backside off the floor. Lift only your buttocks, not your back, as this defeats the purpose of this exercise. Lower back to the floor and repeat. This is quite an advanced exercise. If you find it too difficult, use your hands to help – push down slightly into the mat to help your stomach muscles lift your backside off the mat. This exercise works the rectus abdominis.

Upper Back

Lie face down and place your hands next to your ears. Get someone to hold your heels and lift your head and shoulders off the floor. Some people will be more flexible in this area than others. I recommend that your face should not be lifted more than seven to twelve centimetres off the ground. Lower to the ground, making sure that you relax your muscles, especially your buttocks, then repeat. An easier version, and one for which you shouldn't need anyone holding your legs, is to do the exercise as outlined above but with your arms down by your sides instead of by your ears. This exercise works the erector spinae muscles, the main function of which is to provide your trunk with stability.

Lower Back

Lie face down, hands resting near your temples as above or by your side. Keeping your legs straight raise both your feet a few centimetres off the floor. Hold for a second and return to the floor. This exercise also works the erector spinae.

Obliques

Lying on your back, with your knees up, place one foot on the other leg at the knee. Put the arm on the same side as the raised foot on your stomach. Place the other arm on the side of your head, come up and across with this arm to the opposite knee, trying to touch it, then return to the ground. Repeat on the other side.

Reach Ups

Lying flat, lift up your legs until your feet are straight up above your hips. Crossing your feet, reach up with your hands and touch your feet.

Alternates

This is just a combination of the thigh slide and the heel touch doing one of each alternately.

Upper Body

On joining Chelsea I was surprised to find the numbers of players that neglected their upper bodies. I wasn't looking for huge muscular footballers with the physiques of Linford Christie, but when you're shoulder to shoulder with someone challenging for the ball, that extra bit of strength in the shoulders and arms could help you win that challenge.

Bernard Lambourde, a new player from France, was unfortunately injured in his first game at Kingstonians. It was quite a serious injury, and he had to take a lot of time out while it healed. He spent a lot of that time with me in the gym. While we were there it was noticeable that he had very little upper body strength. I told him that he should be working on this part of his physique, that it was weak and he needed to strengthen it up to play football here. Maybe it was the way I said it or maybe he didn't quite understand what I was saying but he got quite defensive and insisted that he could take care of himself, so I left him alone. Some weeks later, after his first Premiership game, he sought me out as the players were leaving the field and said, 'Weights! Ade, I need weights!' We have been working on strengthening his upper body ever since.

In athletics we had to be strong in the upper body because it had to act as a counterbalance for our legs. For a sprinter, it was important to work each part of the body equally. A sprint race is over in a matter of seconds; a footballer has to keep going for 90 minutes. What we are aiming for is a strong and fit footballer player – an athlete who combines endurance and power.

Shoulders

Sides/Lateral Raises

Take a dumb-bell in each hand with a firm grip. Placing your arms at your sides, palms inwards, raise both arms at the same time, keeping them slightly bent at the elbows until the dumbbells are at shoulder height. Once there lower them down back to your sides and repeat.

Fronts/Shoulder Raises

Take a pair of dumb-bells, both hands in front of you, palms facing inwards, dumb-bells resting on your thighs. Lift one arm at a time to shoulder height, keeping the elbow slightly bent, and return to the starting position.

Shoulder Press

Taking dumb-bells in both hands, place your hands by your ears, palms facing to your head. Push the weights above your head until your arms are straight, making sure that you keep your arms in the same plane as your body and your back straight. Don't lean back. Bring your arms back down to your ears and repeat. You can do this exercise standing or seated.

Shoulder Press/Fixed Machine

Taking a good seated position with the bar parallel to your ears push the bar above your head until your arms are straight. Lower back to starting position and repeat.

Chest

Bench Press

There are two forms of bench press: the 'Free Bench' – where the bar is not an integral part of the bench, and the 'Fixed Bench' – which is an integral piece of gym machinery. The free bench should only be used with a training partner acting as a spotter, helping lift the weight off and back onto its cradle, and giving you a bit of help if you're close to failure. The fixed bench can be done alone. In either case, take a good grip on the bar, hands slightly wider than shoulder width apart. Lower the bar to the chest so that the bar touches the lower part of the chest just below your nipples. Drive the weight back up, straightening your arms, and repeat. Make sure that the arch of your back stays flat by putting your feet up on the end of the bench.

Fixed Bench Press

Free Bench

Press Ups

This exercise works most of the muscles in the upper body and can be adjusted to increase the difficulty. Lying face down, place your hands just below your shoulders, at an equal distance from the middle of your body.

Straighten your arms and go up onto your feet, so that only your hands and toes are in contact with the floor. Keep your body in a straight line, don't allow your backside to wave around in the air, or your hips to sag towards the floor. Now, bend your elbows and lower yourself close to the floor without actually touching it. Then straighten your arms and press yourself back up to the starting position.

If you find this difficult, try keeping your knees on the floor, tucking your feet up behind you. Still keep your trunk straight again and do the press up as before.

This exercise is a great supplement to the bench press and should be done in addition to any other chest exercises. It also has the advantage of being an exercise that you can do pretty much anywhere.

Back

Lat Pull-Down

This exercise works latissimus dorsi, the muscles that run down your sides under your arms, and around the ribbed section of your back. Your biceps also act as synergists in this exercise, so don't have done biceps curls before you do lat pull-downs. In the gym the lat pull-down machine is the one with a small seat on which you sit, facing the weight stack, with a wide-handled bar above your head.

There are two basic variations:

① Wide grip/palms facing away

Sit comfortably (there will probably be pads for you to slide your knees under) and take a firm, wide grip on the bar (as in picture one). Now, pull the bar down, behind your head until it's level with your ears, and return to the starting position.

② Narrow grip/palms facing inwards

Taking a firm grip in the middle of the bar, palms towards you (as in picture two), lean back slightly, and maintaining this body position (i.e. don't throw your body back to help you) pull the bar down to your chest, just below the nipples and return to starting position. There is more biceps involvement with this variation.

Triceps

The triceps are the muscles on the back of the upper arm. Such muscles need to be worked to balance other muscles that are more directly involved in football. A simple 'Triceps Dip' is sufficient to maintain strength in this muscle and it will also work your shoulders and chest. Sit on a bench and place your hands on the bench by your sides. Make sure your legs are straight out in front of you with only your heels on the floor. Taking your weight on your hands, lift your backside off the bench. Lower your body so that your elbows bend to a 90 degree angle, keeping your back close the bench, then straighten your arms, lifting your body up again. If doing this exercise with straight legs is too difficult, bend your knees slightly.

Biceps

Dumb-bell biceps curls

The biceps are the muscles at the front of the forearm .Take a dumb-bell in each hand. Hold them by your sides so that your palms are facing in to your body. Keeping your elbows by your sides, curl the weight up to your shoulders at the same time turning your wrist until the dumb-bells (and your palms) are facing your shoulders. Return to the starting position reversing the twist in your wrist. The rotation here gives your biceps a little extra work.

Barbell biceps curls (21s)

Take a barbel in both hands, with a shoulder-width grip, curl the bar up until you have a 90 degree angle at the elbow, and return to starting position. Make sure you straighten your arms out at the bottom of the movement and keep your elbows tucked in to your sides. Do seven reps.

Then, without stopping, start with a 90 degree angle at the elbow, and curl the bar up to your shoulders, lowering it back down to the 90 degree position, and then back up to your shoulders. Do seven reps. Finally from the bottom position with your arms straight, curl the bar all the way up to your shoulders and return back to the bottom for another seven reps. This way you will have done 21 reps in total.

2. Circuits for body strength

An alternative for those who don't have access to weights or a gym is circuit training. Traditionally this involves creating a circuit of exercises, each of which relies on body weight to provide the resistance, rather than machinery.

Circuits represent perhaps the best form of exercise for children from the ages of eight to seventeen. Theories that oppose strength training for children centre on the problems that can occur when children over-train. When you do any kind of resistance exercise, stress is placed on the tendons that attach muscles to bones. In children the bones are still growing and the areas from which growth occurs often correspond with muscle/tendon attachments. The result of excessive stress can be retardation of growth and/or bony growths around the sites where tendons and bones connect. Osgood Schlatter's disease, for example, is a bony growth on the front of the tibia just below the knee, and is a consequence of too much hard running at too early an age. The best rule of thumb for under-seventeens is to keep your training fun. This may sound pretty corny, but I don't suppose anyone would look forward to having to quit their sport at an early age because of over-training in previous years. These days sports, and especially football, are becoming increasingly competitive. The stakes are getting higher and higher and the pressure to win, ever greater. So listen to your body and don't overdo it.

As part of the circuts you can do all the abdominals, back exercises and triceps dips that I have described earlier along with the following:

All Body

Squat Thrusts/Burpees
A great exercise working the upper and lower body at the same time. The first exercise leads on to the second so I will describe the squat thrust first.

To start these exercises get into the same starting position as the press up. But this time keeping the arms straight, tuck the knees up to the chest by jumping your feet forward, making sure that they leave the floor as you move your feet forward. Immediately return them to the starting position and repeat. To do a burpee repeat the first phase of the squat thrust to when the knees are tucked in then stand upright. Next, fall back down onto the floor and resume the 'press-up start position'. This exercise can be made more difficult by adding a jump to the standing up phase.

Leg Exercises

I use two leg exercises in circuit training. The first is the step up. Using a knee-high bench, place a foot on top of the bench keeping your other foot on the floor. Step up onto the bench and then step back down onto the floor with the foot that was on the bench at the start. The important thing is to have one foot on the bench at all times. This way there's less chance of the bench toppling over, and because you're doing it slowly it will be more effective as a quad strengthener.

The second leg exercise is the free squat:

Stand upright facing away from a chair, feet shoulder width apart and pointing forwards. Make sure that if you were to sit down onto the chair the angle behind your knee is never less than 90 degrees. With your arms folded sit down until your backside just touches the seat. Then stand up again and repeat.

Circuit Formations

The structure of your circuit must be geared towards quality of work, rather than quantity. A badly structured circuit can overload a body part and reduce the quality of the exercises you subsequently do. It's a similar principle to that which applies to weight training where you exercise larger muscle groups first.

The exercises can be done for a number of seconds (e.g. 30), or for a set number of repetitions (e.g. 20-30). If you're coaching a team of varying abilities, it's probably best to use time/seconds rather than repetitions. On the other hand, if you think some players are short on motivation, making everyone do a set number of repetitions rewards those who are already fitter, whilst giving the less fit a specific goal to aim for. Yet another alternative is to mix it up – some exercises are done for time, others for reps. Take 15 seconds rest between each exercise.

Here are a few examples of a well-structured circuit:

Jogging on the Spot	1 min
Press Ups	20 reps
Headers on Spot	30 secs
Jogging on the Spot	30 secs
Abdominals	20 reps
Burpees	20 reps
Jogging on the Spot	30 secs
Triceps Dip	20 reps
Back Exercises	20 reps
Jogging on the Spot	30 secs
Squats	20 reps
Abdominals	20 reps

A group can do this type of circuit together, with each individual doing the same exercises at the same time. Alternatively, players can move round from one training area, or station, to another doing a different exercise at each stop.

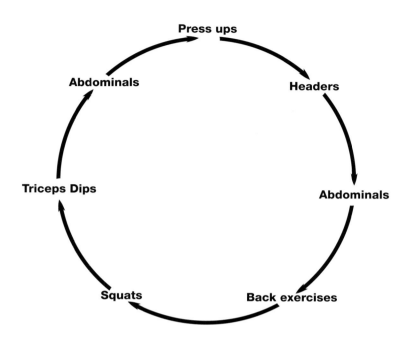

All circuit exercises will have to differ in terms of sets, reps and time duration according to age and strength. Use the following table as a rough guide only.

This I think is a good guide to all circuit exercises for the growing football player. Sets/reps/duration in a circuit for mature players should be decided according to their individual and collective abilities.

Exercise Sets	Ages 8-12	Ages 13-16
Upper Body 2	5-10 reps	10-15 reps
Abdominals 3	10-15 reps	15-25 reps
Leg Exercises 3	8-10 reps	10-15 reps

3. Pylometrics

PYLOMETRICS ARE TAXING ENOUGH FOR A TRAINED ATHLETE. I WOULD ABSOLUTELY NOT RECOMMEND THEM FOR ANYONE UNDER SEVENTEEN.

This is a form of training that improves the explosive strength in your legs, which is beneficial for both your sprinting and explosive jumping (headers). The movements have to be carried out quickly. The emphasis needs to be on speed, so reaction time and power are the key to reaping maximum benefit. Pylometrics is an advanced form of training. If you are not already very well-conditioned, don't do them. Additionally, if you have any injuries – particularly to your knees or back, pylometrics are also best avoided.

Two-Footed Bounding

Always warm up thoroughly making sure that special attention is paid to the lower back, quads, hamstrings, and calves.

Make sure the back remains as straight as possible during all exercises.

Always do these exercises on a firm but yielding surface such as grass or a sprung wooden floor.

One Golden Rule: Spend Minimum Time on the Ground.

Double Touch Jumps

This is a simple exercise but can be difficult to execute. However, with persistence and practice it can be achieved. Standing upright, jump up as high as you can, bending the knees to get the initial power for the jump. While in the air straighten your body with your arms by your sides. As you land, jump up again immediately, bending the knees as little as possible. The transition from landing the first jump to taking the second should be as short as possible.

Drop Jumps

Place a box or chair on the floor and climb onto it. Drop off it onto the floor and then jump up immediately as high as you can, mimicking a header. Climb back up on the platform and repeat. The higher the platform, the harder the exercise will be. A good starting height from which to jump would be about 1.3 metres.

Two-Footed Bounding

This is a simple two-footed jump incorporated into a short shuttle run. Place cones or small hurdles at regular intervals to be cleared on each run. At each marker jump high enough to tuck the feet up underneath the body while in the air. Remember, keep the back straight and use the arms at the start of the jump to help with the initial momentum.

Running Bounds

Run slowly using a long, loping stride. With each stride try to get as high in the air as possible while still moving forwards.

There s a price to pay for all this leg strengthening and that price is fatigue and soreness in the muscles. This lets you know that your muscles have been pushed beyond their normal capabilities. Painful though it may be at first, it's a natural consequence of strength development.

Great attention has to be paid to the timing and frequency of these sessions so that you are not tired before a match. During the pre-season period we do at least two pylometric sessions a week with at least two days rest in between each session. In-season we do one session a week, preferably at the beginning of the week when there is no midweek game.

Part 5

Diet

Ten years ago, British professional footballers ate whatever they wanted, from full fry-ups for breakfast to steak and chips before a game. Tea, coffee, lager, beer and fizzy drinks were drunk in great quantities before, during and after games and training. There was a lack of knowledge in the football community about nutrition and the effects that different food groups and drinks have on the body. As time has gone on and knowledge has increased, the dietary habits of footballers have changed. Nutritionists have been brought in to clubs to give advice and physios are now finding themselves responsible for the collective diet of the players in the squad.

When Ruud Gullit took over from Glen Hoddle as Chelsea manager, one of the first things he did, in conjunction with club physios Mike Banks and Terry Byrne, was to change the food available at the training ground canteen. Out went the pies and chips and all fried food, to be replaced with grilled chicken, fish, pasta, rice, jacket potatoes, fresh bread, fresh vegetables and fruit. Cooked breakfasts were out – toast, cereals and fruit were in. These dietary measures are also enforced when the squad is staying in hotels for away matches.

A healthy diet is an essential part of any fitness programme. That doesn't mean you have to deny yourself everything you enjoy and live on salad and water, however. By following a few simple rules and being more aware of what you eat and how it is cooked, you can feel fitter and healthier and increase your energy and endurance levels on the pitch.

1. Foods to eat – foods to avoid

Food is your body's petrol, and the better the quality of fuel you put in the better the performance you will get from your body.

There are three sources of energy in food: fats, proteins and carbohydrates:

FATS, which are found in meats, dairy products, eggs, nuts and oils actually contain the most energy, but despite being crammed with energy they are only beneficial to us if we are doing low intensity exercises such as jogging, and no good for higher intensity exercises such as sprinting. Eating too much fatty food is not good for the heart as it raises the cholesterol levels and can cause health problems. Fat which is not burned up will be stored in the body causing weight gain and mobility problems.

To reduce the fat content in your diet, cut down on the whole milk dairy products, milk, butter, cream and cheese – use skimmed milk and low fat alternatives; bake, grill or boil food rather than frying; cut down on junk food such as confectionery, chips, pies and burgers; go for fish or skinless chicken rather than fatty meats such as bacon or pork chops.

PROTEINS, found in fish, meat, vegetables and dairy products help with muscle building and strength that is essential for any player. However, it is difficult for the body to convert protein to energy, so proteins provide only a small percentage of the body's energy.

CARBOHYDRATES are the best source of energy for the body. They provide most of the energy for aerobic and anaerobic activity. There are two types of carbohydrate, simple and complex. Simple carbohydrates are basic sugars, which can be found in fizzy drinks, biscuits, sweets, cakes and similar foods. They are also found in fruit such as bananas. The body can convert simple carbohydrates to energy very quickly so they can be useful for replacing energy which you have used up during a game. However, if not burned off they will be converted into fat in the body.

Complex carbohydrates are found in foods such as wholemeal bread, whole potatoes, wholemeal pasta, brown rice, wholemeal cereals, and vegetables. They are not as readily converted to fat as the simple carbohydrates.

Before exercise, it is important that your body has a good supply of carbohydrates to produce the energy it needs. This can be achieved through carbo-loading – eating more than your normal amount of complex carbohydrates for at least two days before a game. This ensures that high levels of energy are in the body and the muscles by the time of the game and are ready and waiting to be used up. Taking an extra helping of rice or pasta with your meal in the days before a big match might give you that extra burst of energy on the pitch.

On the day of a game a good balanced meal at least three hours before playing is recommended, allowing sufficient time for digestion and proper absorption of the food into the body.

Luca Vialli's meal before a game normally consists of a plate of plain rice with some Parmesan cheese and a dash of olive oil for flavouring. This is followed by a grilled skinless chicken breast accompanied by some vegetables.

Graham Le Saux usually has plain pasta with a small piece of grilled chicken, with water as his pre-match drink.

After a game most of the body's carboydrate energy should have been used up. For the body to recover it must be refilled, either with complex or simple carbohydrates. Ideally this should be done within two hours of playing. The Chelsea squad snack on high carbohydrate bars and drinks immediately after a match and follow that up with a proper meal high in complex carbohydrates.

Dennis Wise is a biscuit freak and can eat a whole packet of biscuits on the coach back to London after an away game.. He needs this supply of simple carbohydrates to restore his depleted energy resources after a gruelling match.

2. Drinks

During exercise the body loses a lot of fluid through sweat and breath, and this has to be replaced. Dehydration and the ensuing rise in body temperature can cause fatigue. Drinking water is good for rehydration but since you are losing carbohydrates as well as fluids when exercising, it's a good idea to go for a carbo drink such as Lucozade Sport and Gatorade. These drinks contain glucose – a form of simple carbohydrate that can be assimilated more easily into the body than the sugars found in ordinary fizzy drinks or squashes. An even better option is isotonic drinks, which are specially designed for quick absorption. These drinks also contain the important minerals which are lost through sweat.

Opinions concerning the amounts of fluid to drink before and during a game vary. The most important thing to remember is never drink to the stage where you are bloated. I would recommend that you have two to three mouthfuls of water or a carbo drink after the warm up, about five minutes before beginning to play. At half time drink around three-quarters of a pint.

When training stop every half an hour or so for a drink. After a game or training drink at least 100-200 grams or 3-7 fluid oz of fluid.

It is good to avoid alcohol after a game. Alcohol is a diuretic which means it will add to the problems of dehydration.

Conclusion

Whether you are a professional player or just enjoy a kick around in the park at the weekend, it is extremely important that you prepare your body properly before playing. That's why I have made stretching and mobility exercises a key part of this book. As the Chelsea lads often remind me, these exercises can seem rather tedious when you want to get on with the game, but they must be done if you are going to get the best out of your body on the pitch, and avoid injury.

Football fitness training used to be ruled by the belief that the harder you run, the fitter you become. Some people still believe this, but scientific advances over the years have proved that specially tailored exercises can do more to improve a player's endurance, speed, agility and reactions on the pitch than long runs alone ever could. These are the exercises that I have outlined in sections two and three of *Football Fitness*.

For the best results these exercises should be undertaken at different times in the season and you should alternate between training for endurance and stamina and speed, agility and reaction exercises. I hope that the variety of exercises I have described will make your training sessions more fun and interesting too.

Weights, circuit training and pylometric training if necessary will strengthen and condition your body, making you a faster, stronger, fitter and ultimately a better football player. Training as a team will improve team play and morale too.

Finally a good diet will help you feel at your best and have the energy you need to play.

Well, that's about it. I hope this book has been of some value to you, enabling you to enjoy your football even more as you get fitter and hopefully have fewer aches, pains and injuries. Don't expect overnight results, it takes time, patience and hard work but the results will be worth it in the end.

Good luck, good training and most of all, enjoy yourself.

Acknowledgements

Many thanks to my mum and dad, my sister Adeola and girlfriend Tracey for all their support. Without them this book wouldn't have been possible. Thanks to the staff at Chelsea Football Club; Ruud Gullit for giving me the chance to bring my knowledge to football; Jon Nicholson for taking the photographs for this book and all the chaps in the team for keeping me on my toes.